The fun way to learn!

Razzamajazz bassoon

SARAH WATTS

ANTIQUARISCH

kevin mayhew

We hope you enjoy *Razzamajazz for Bassoon*.
Further copies of this and our many other books are available
from your local Kevin Mayhew stockist.

In case of difficulty, or to request a catalogue,
please contact the publisher direct by writing to:

The Sales Department
KEVIN MAYHEW LTD
Buxhall
Stowmarket
Suffolk IP14 3BW

Phone 01449 737978
Fax 01449 737834
E-mail info@kevinmayhewltd.com

First published in Great Britain in 2003 by Kevin Mayhew Ltd.

© Copyright 2003 Kevin Mayhew Ltd.

ISBN 1 84417 044 6
ISMN M 57024 181 1
Catalogue No: 3611738

0 1 2 3 4 5 6 7 8 9

Cover design: Angela Selfe
Music setter: Donald Thomson
Proof reader: Tracy Cook

Printed and bound in Great Britain

Contents

A note from the composer

This is a fun book of jazzy pieces with a 'feel good' accompaniment to encourage you in the early stages of learning.

Although *Razzamajazz* is not a tutor, I hope you will enjoy learning the pieces and benefit from them.

SARAH WATTS

Introducing E

This is where it goes on the music

To play E press the keys coloured black

Right hand

Lef *ha...*

ONE NOTE SWING

NOTE USED - E

Swing ($\quad$ = 124)

5

8

here's D

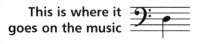

This is where it goes on the music

To play D press the keys coloured black

Left hand

Right hand

TWO AT TWILIGHT

NOTES USED: E, D

5

now for C

This is where it goes on the music

To play C press the keys coloured black

Right hand

STARDOM WALTZ

NOTES USED - E, D, C

($\quad$ = 120)

mp legato

mp

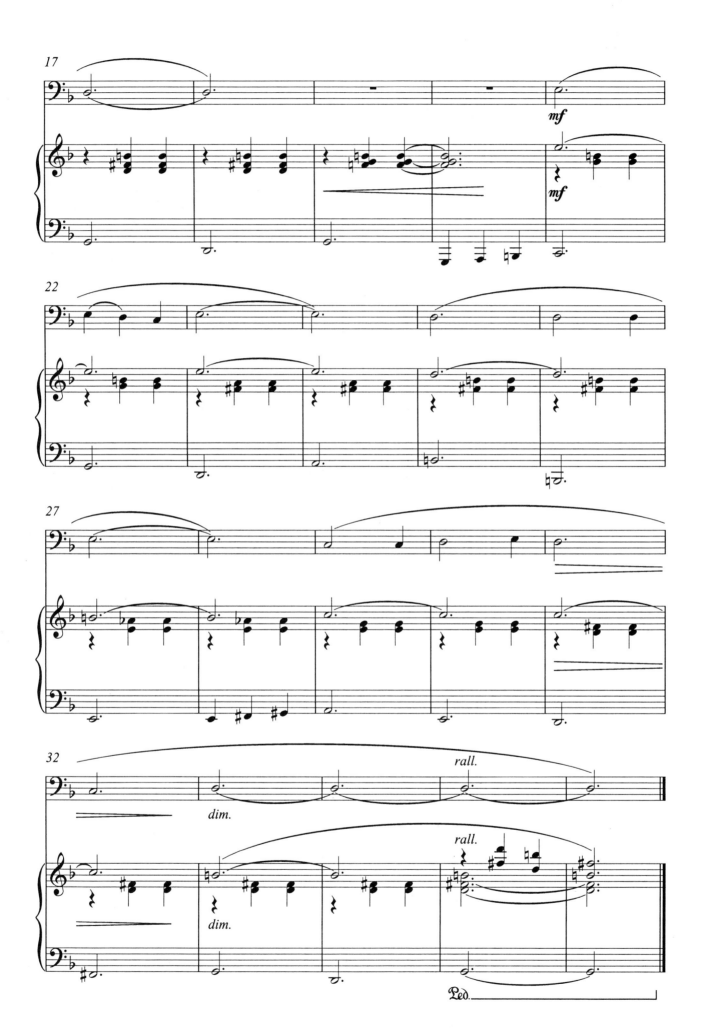

STRIPY CAT CRAWL

NOTES USED - E, D

8

...and now F

This is where it goes on the music

To play F press the keys coloured black

Left hand

Right hand

MR COOL

NOTES USED - E, D, C, F

Swing (♩ = 130)

Optional vocals (spoken):

6

Yeh!   U-huh!   Hit it!

11

That's cool!   Yeh!

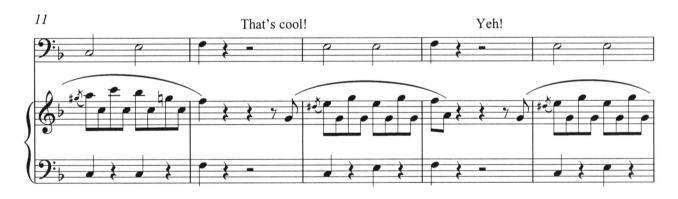

16

U-huh!   Hit it!   I'm done!

KIM'S BALLAD

NOTES USED - E, D, C, F

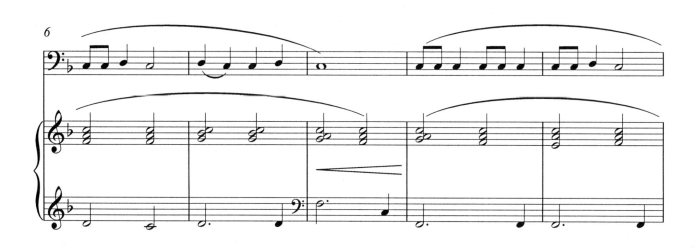

and next G

To play G press the keys coloured black

This is where it goes on the music

MOVIE BUSTER

NOTES USED - E, D, C, F, G

MELLOW OUT

NOTES USED - E, D, C, F, G

and on to A

This is where it goes on the music

To play A press the keys coloured black

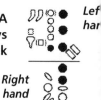

Lef han

Right hand

WATER LILIES

NOTES USED - E, D, C, F, G, A

Razzamajazz
bassoon

SARAH WATTS

Introducing E

This is where it goes on the music

To play E press the keys coloured black

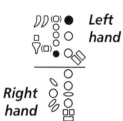

Left hand

Right hand

ONE NOTE SWING

NOTE USED - E

Swing (♩ = 124)

here's D

This is where it goes on the music

To play D press the keys coloured black

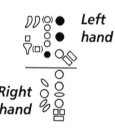

Left hand

Right hand

TWO AT TWILIGHT

NOTES USED - E, D

(♩ = 112)

p

now for C

This is where it goes on the music

To play C press the keys coloured black

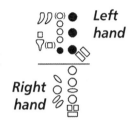

STARDOM WALTZ

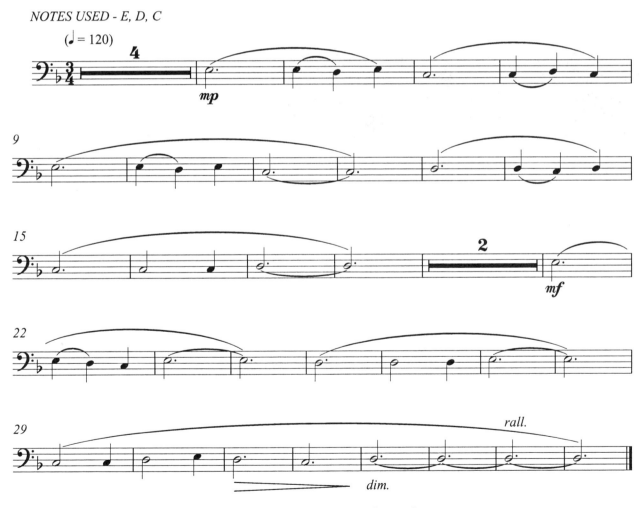

STRIPY CAT CRAWL

NOTES USED - E, D

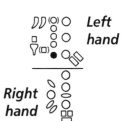

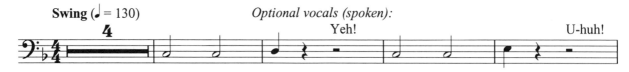

MR COOL

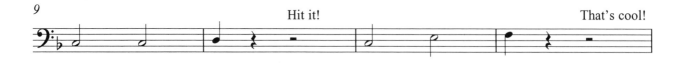

Yeh!   U-huh!

Hit it!   I'm done!

KIM'S BALLAD

NOTES USED - E, D, C, F

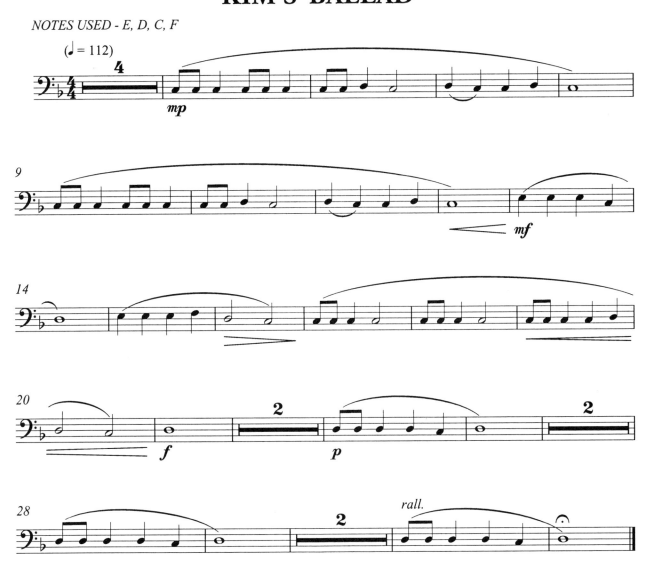

and next G

This is where it goes on the music

To play G press the keys coloured black

Left hand

Right hand

MOVIE BUSTER

NOTES USED - E, D, C, F, G

Driving (♩ = 150)

MELLOW OUT

NOTES USED - E, D, C, F, G

and on to A

To play A press the keys coloured black

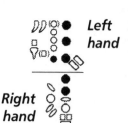

Left hand

Right hand

WATER LILIES

NOTES USED - E, D, C, F, G, A

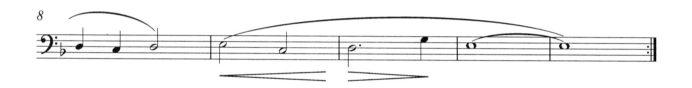

here's low G

To play low G press the keys coloured black

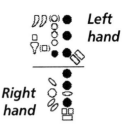

Left hand

Right hand

This is where it goes on the music

TEN TOE TAPPER

NOTES USED - E, D, C, F, G, A, low G

Swing (♩ = 158)

mf

9

13 *Tap dance! (or Woodblock solo)*

mf

19

24

p

PLAY OF LIGHT

NOTES USED - G, A, B, C, D, E, low G, F

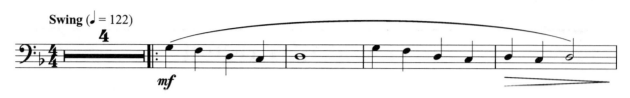

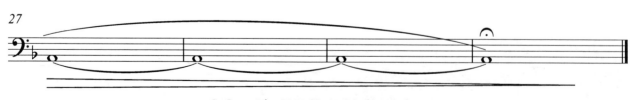

now for B♭

This is where it goes on the music

To play B♭ press the keys coloured black

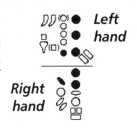

Left hand

Right hand

SEA SPARKLE

NOTES USED - E, D, C, F, G, A, B♭

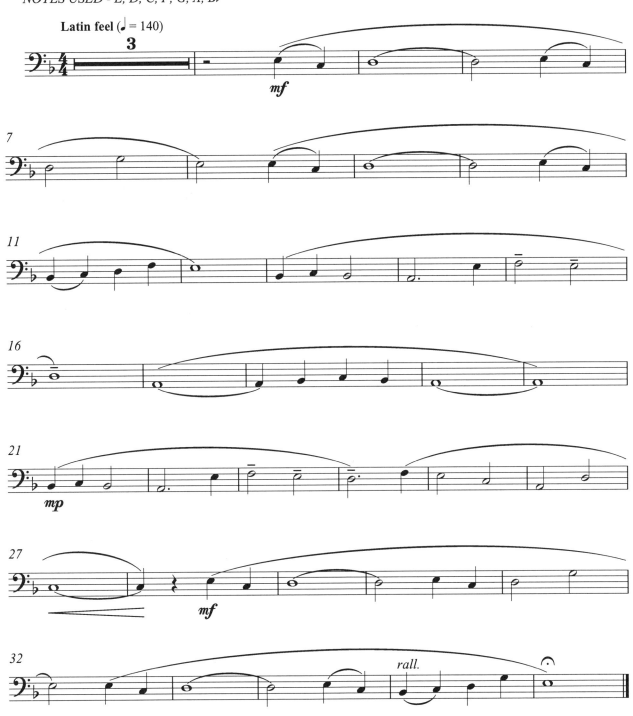

© Copyright 2003 Kevin Mayhew Ltd.
It is illegal to photocopy music.

and now E♭

This is where it goes on the music

To play E♭ press the keys coloured black

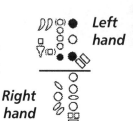

Left hand

Right hand

MORNING IN MOSCOW

NOTES USED - D, C, F, A, low G, B♭, E♭

and finally B♮

To play B♮
press the keys
coloured black

Left hand

Right hand

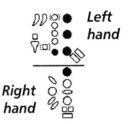

This is where
it goes on
the music

SHRIMP SHUFFLE

NOTES USED - G, A, B, C, D, E, low G, F, B♭, E♭, B♮

BANANA TANGO

NOTES USED - E, D, C, F, G, A, B♭, B♮

14

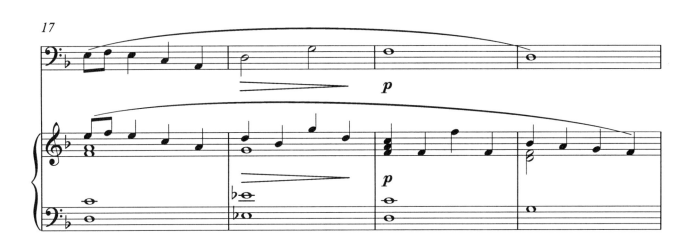

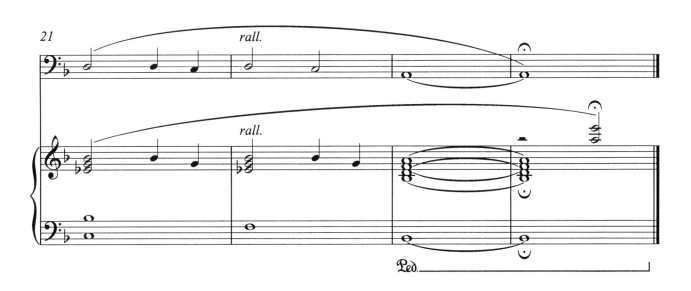

here's low G

To play low G press the keys coloured black

Right hand

Left hand

This is where it goes on the music 𝄢

TEN TOE TAPPER

NOTES USED: *E, D, C, F, G, A, low G*

Swing (♩ = 158)

Tap dance! (or woodblock solo)

20

24

now for B♭

This is where it goes on the music 𝄢 ♭

To play B♭ press the keys coloured black

Left hand

Right hand

PLAY OF LIGHT

NOTES USED: E, D, C, F, G, A, low G, B♭

SEA SPARKLE

NOTES USED: E, D, C, F, G, A, B♭

and now E♭

This is where it goes on the music

To play E♭ press the keys coloured black

Right hand

MORNING IN MOSCOW

NOTES USED: D, C, F, A, low G, B♭, E♭

(♩ = 86)

5

9

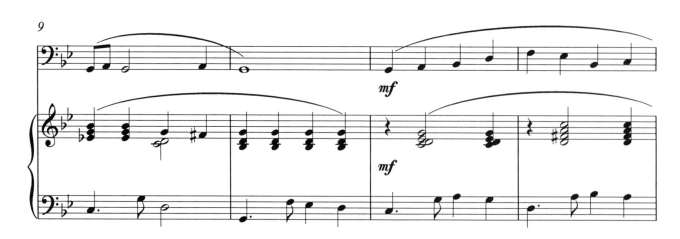

© Copyright 2003 Kevin Mayhew Ltd.
It is illegal to photocopy music.

24

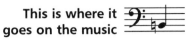

and now B♮

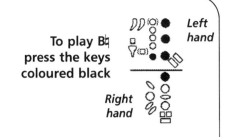

To play B♮
press the keys
coloured black

Left hand

Right hand

This is where it goes on the music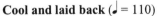

SHRIMP SHUFFLE

NOTES USED - E, D, C, F, G, A, low G, B♭, E♭, B♮

Cool and laid back (♩ = 110)

mp

5

mp

9

Last time to Coda ⊕

Last time to Coda ⊕

BANANA TANGO

NOTES USED: E, D, C, F, G, A, B♭, B♮

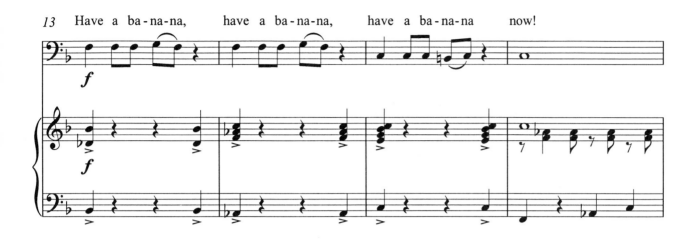

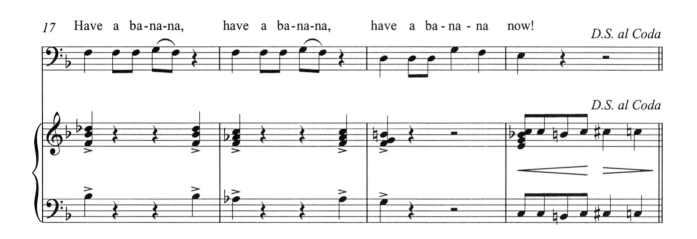